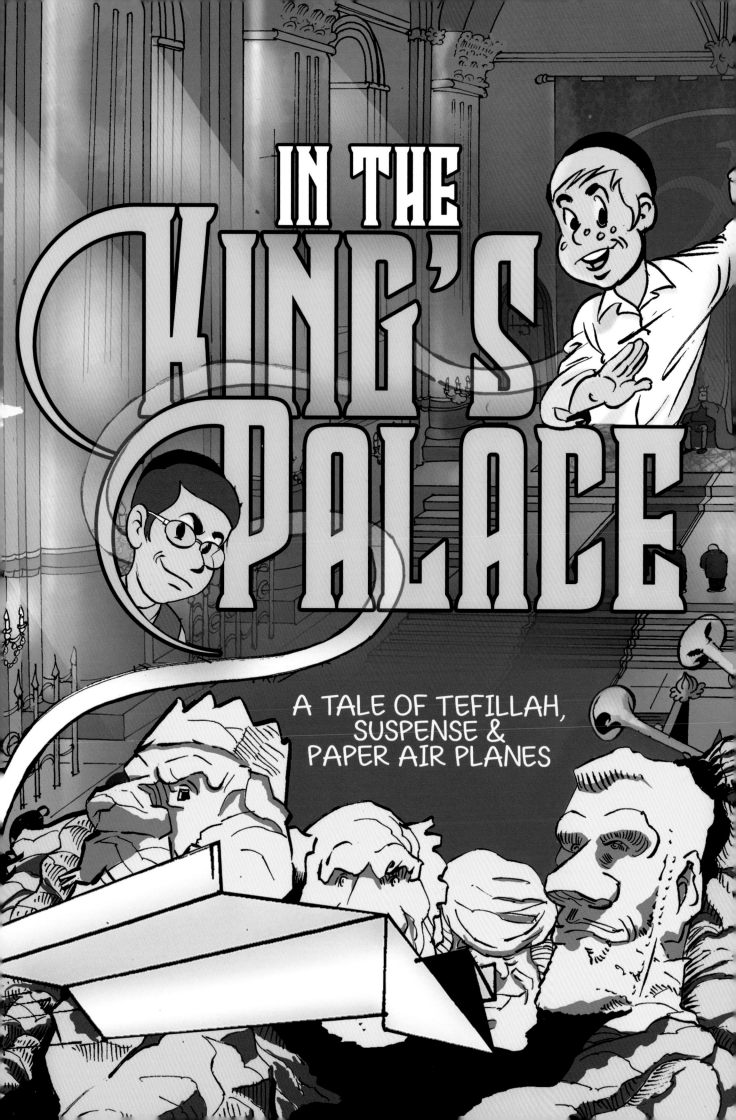

Published by: **Levi Hasofer**

Written by: **Yonah Klein**

Illustrated by: **Jacky Yarhi**

Coloring: **Shneor Yarhi**

Layout: **Shoshana Radunsky**

Distributed by: **Feldheim**

Haskama from
Harav Hagaon
R' Fishel Schachter, *shlita*

פישל שעכטער

Reb Levi has blended a uniquely exciting illustrated story. Woven with striking comical and delightful messages of *emuna* and *achdus*, I am sure it will be a welcome addition to delightfully entertaining *chinnuch* in your homes.

Fishel Schachter

Dear parents and educators:

With deep gratitude to Hashem, we hereby present *In The King's Palace* - a fun read chock full of insights into תפילת שמונה עשרה. There are, of course, many ספרים that explain Shemoneh Esrei in an age-appropriate manner for children. This book, however, allows children to learn about *tefillah* as they enjoy a fun-filled adventure in a fantastic kingdom. The insights into each *bracha* are short and to the point, highlighting one or two aspects of each *bracha* in שמונה עשרה.

The halacha teaches (טור או״ח סי' 101) that "one should accustom himself to have *kavana* at least at the conclusion of each bracha." Our *gedolim* teach that children should at least have in mind the general theme of each *bracha*. As the conclusion of every *bracha* is really a praise to Hashem, rather than a request, we chose insights that stress the praise in these *brachos*. Great care was taken to to find authentic sources for the ideas presented in every *bracha* (see the full list of sources in the back of the book).

We ask Hashem that our readers' *davening* be enhanced by this book, and that they continue to grow in *avodas hatfilla*. May we all be *zoche* to the rewards for עיון תפילה, both in עולם הזה and עולם הבא, speedily and in our days.

We would like to express our deep gratitude to the following people, who's deep professionalism and talent have left their marks on every page of this work:
• First and foremost, to Reb Yaakov (Jacky) Yarhi, whose beautiful and fun illustrations have made this book a work of art.
• His son, Shneor Yarhi, who did a top-notch job on coloring.
• Shoshana Radunsky for text layout. Her patience in the face of constant revisions is legendary.
• We would also like to thank our wives and children for their heartfelt support and love throughout this and all our projects. We are blessed to have you!

We particularly wish to express a heartfelt "thank you" to the many sponsors whose dedications appear in the back of the book. Your generosity has made this project possible - without you, it would have been no more than an idea! May Hashem repay you with health, *nachas* and *parnassa* in abundance.

Acharon acharon chaviv, we thank You, *Ribbono shel Olam*, for creating us, giving us such a wonderful life, the creativity and opportunity to teach and tell stories, and, of course, for the Torah that makes this a story worth telling.

לוּלֵי תוֹרָתְךָ שַׁעֲשֻׁעָי אָז אָבַדְתִּי בְעָנְיִי.

Levi Hasofer   *Yonah Halevi Klein*

And now, young sirs, if you will all follow me, we can visit the gift shop and ice cream stand before you go

What?

It's over already?

I'm afraid so. You were only scheduled in for a brief visit. Perhaps you'll come back another time for the full tour

But, I mean—

Isn't is possible, just maybe—

Any way at all, even for a bit—

We want to see our king!

What?! Of course not! It's impossible!

Please! Just for a second!

We want to tell him how much we appreciate him!

But of course you can't! I'm sorry, but our king is far too important to meet a few children! Do you have any idea how valuable his time is?! Now come along

IN THE KING'S PALACE   13

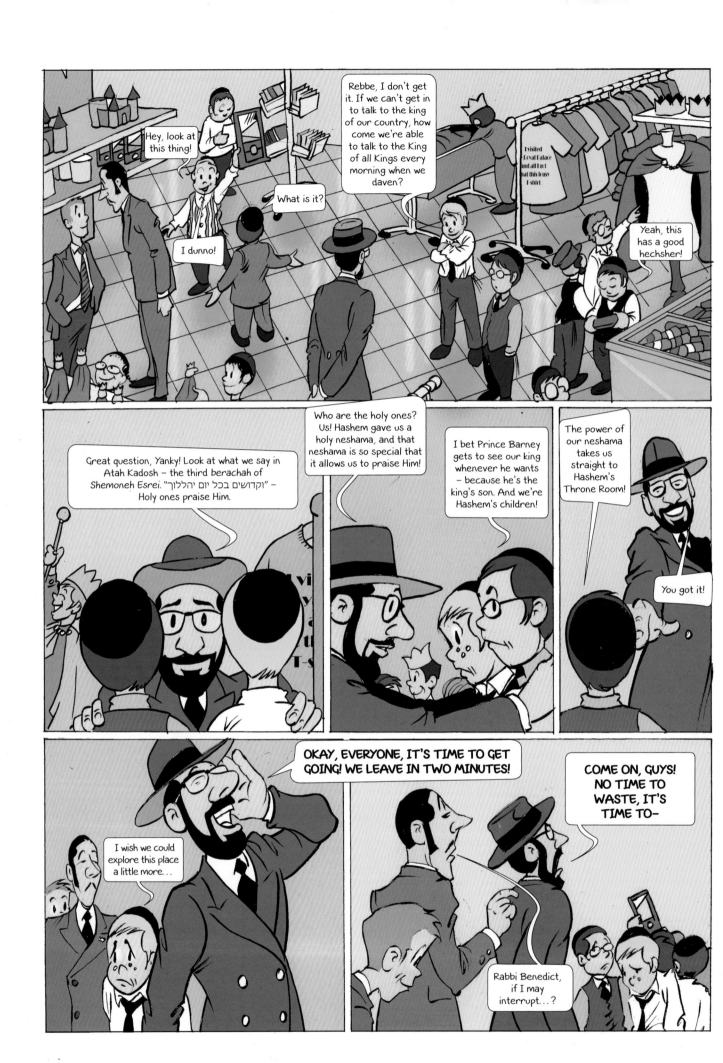

Well, this is where we stop.

YAAAAA!

SCREEEEEETCH!

Why'd you have to stop so fast, Larry?!

Sorry 'bout that, guys. This is the prince's house.

His house? He doesn't live in the palace with his father?

None of the royal family sleep in the main building. That's just for matters of state, entertaining guests, and tourist attractions.

The king and his family each have a house to themselves here, in the back of the royal grounds.

And now, may I present to you, Prince Bernard II!

Known affectionately to his friends as Prince Barney.

Prince Barney! I knew it!

Hi guys! Thanks for coming!

We wouldn't miss it for the world!

Did you have any trouble getting permission?

Well, we have to take notes. And be polite.

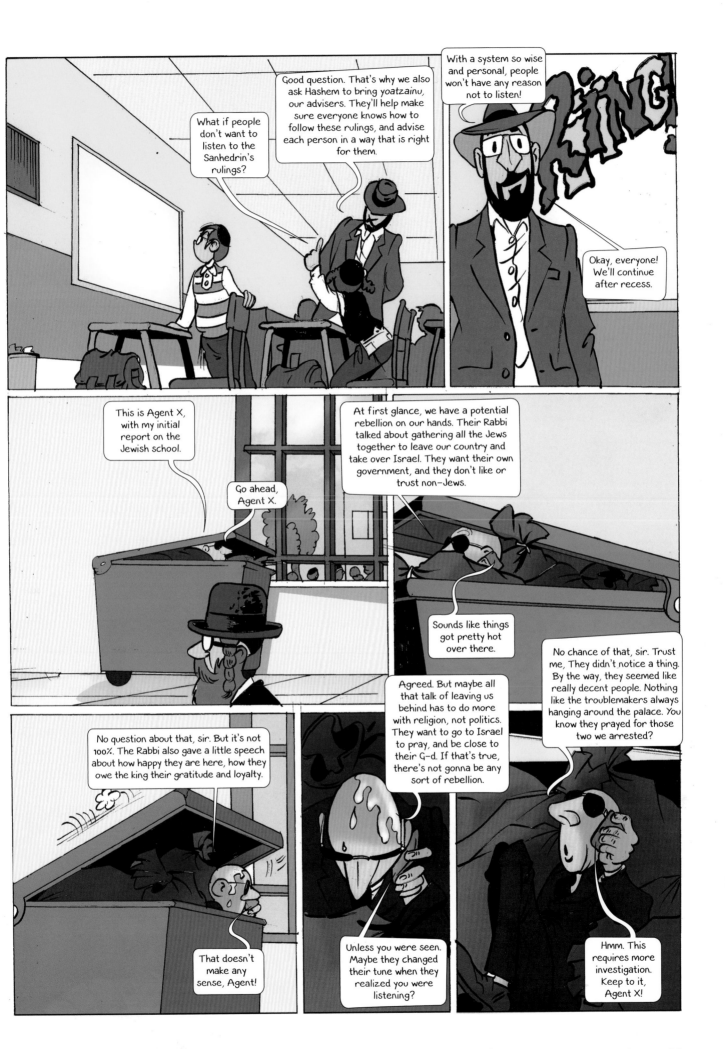

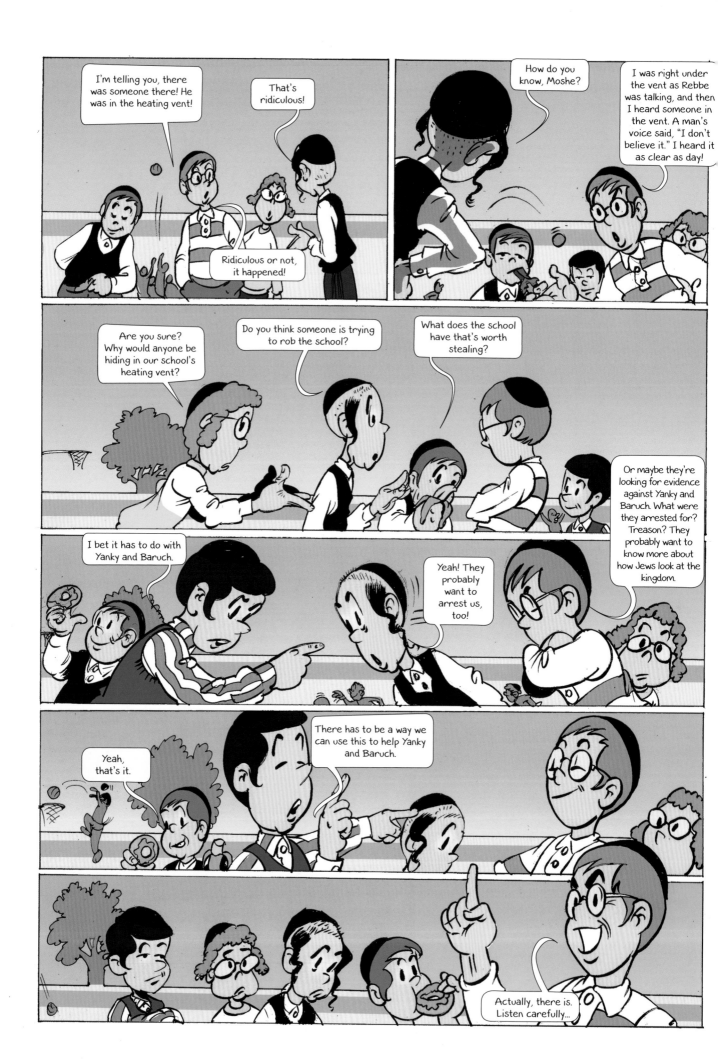

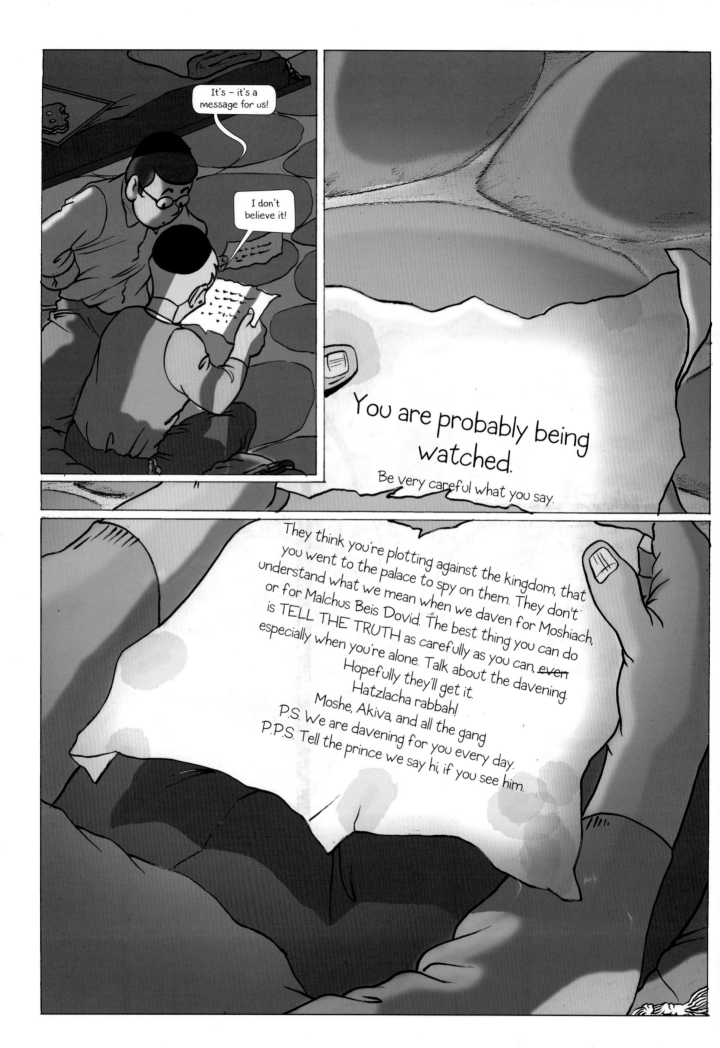

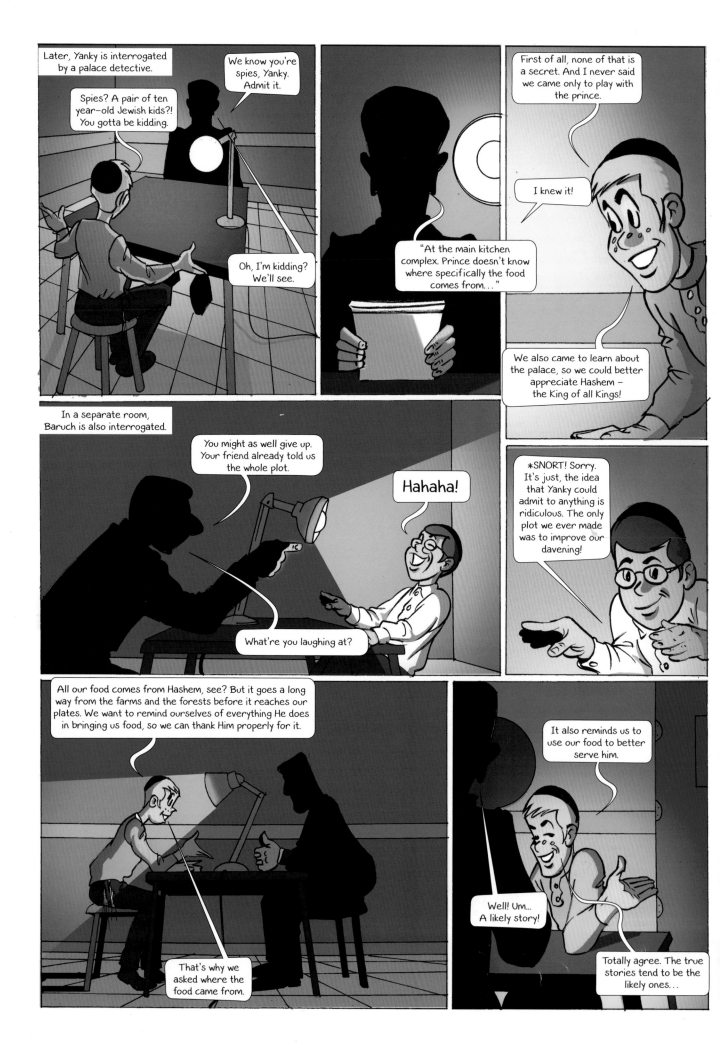

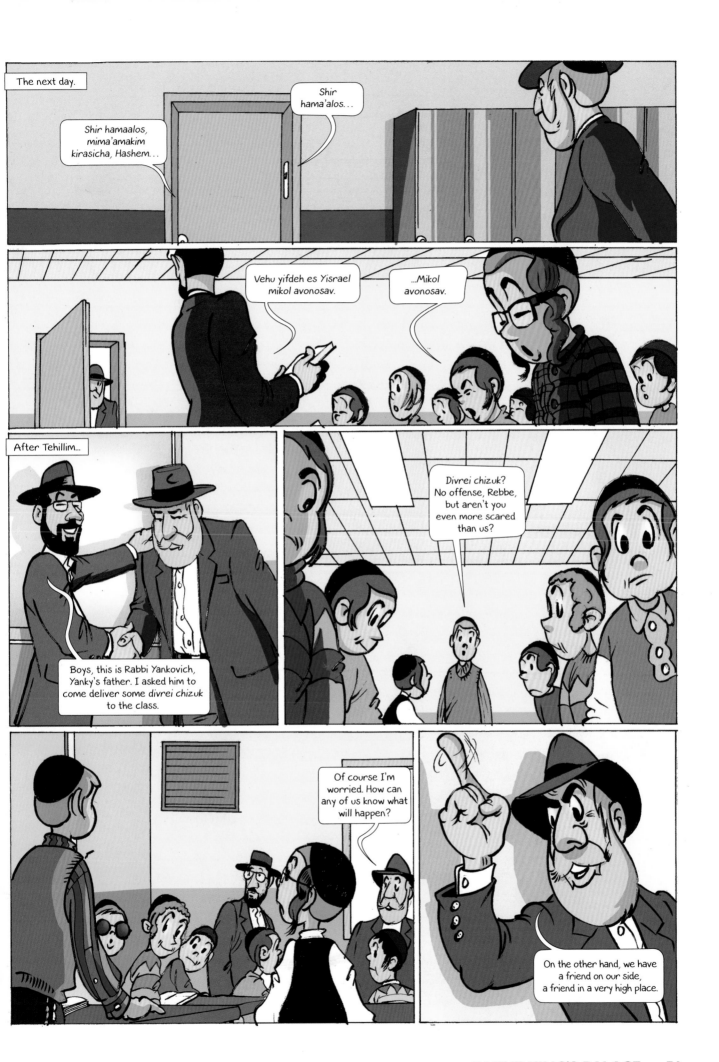

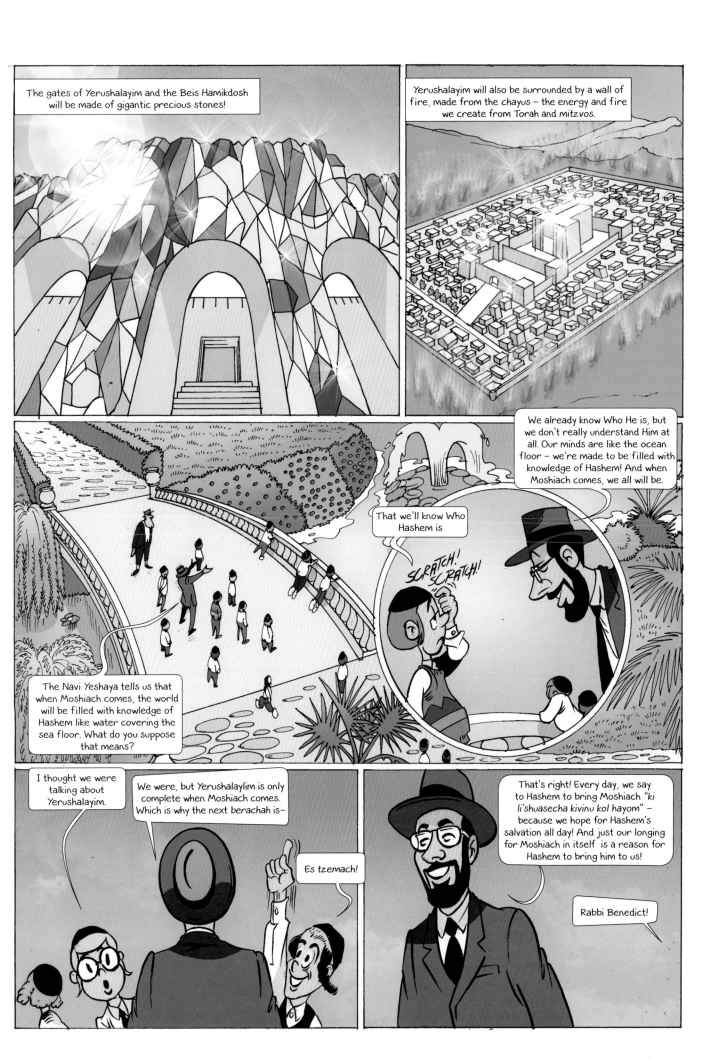

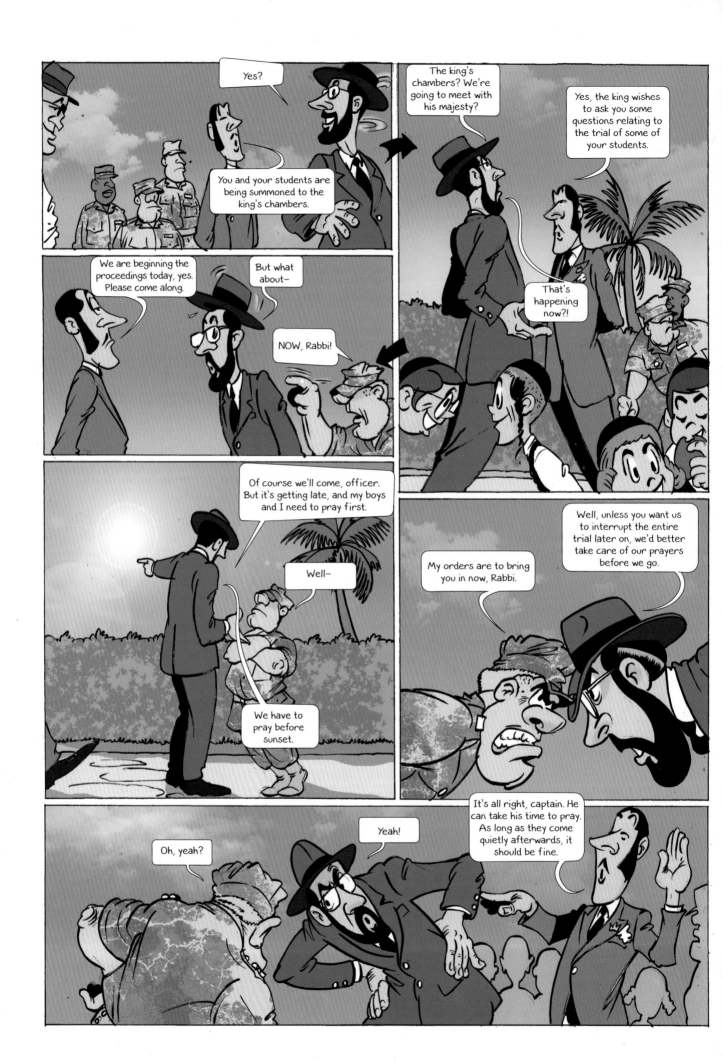

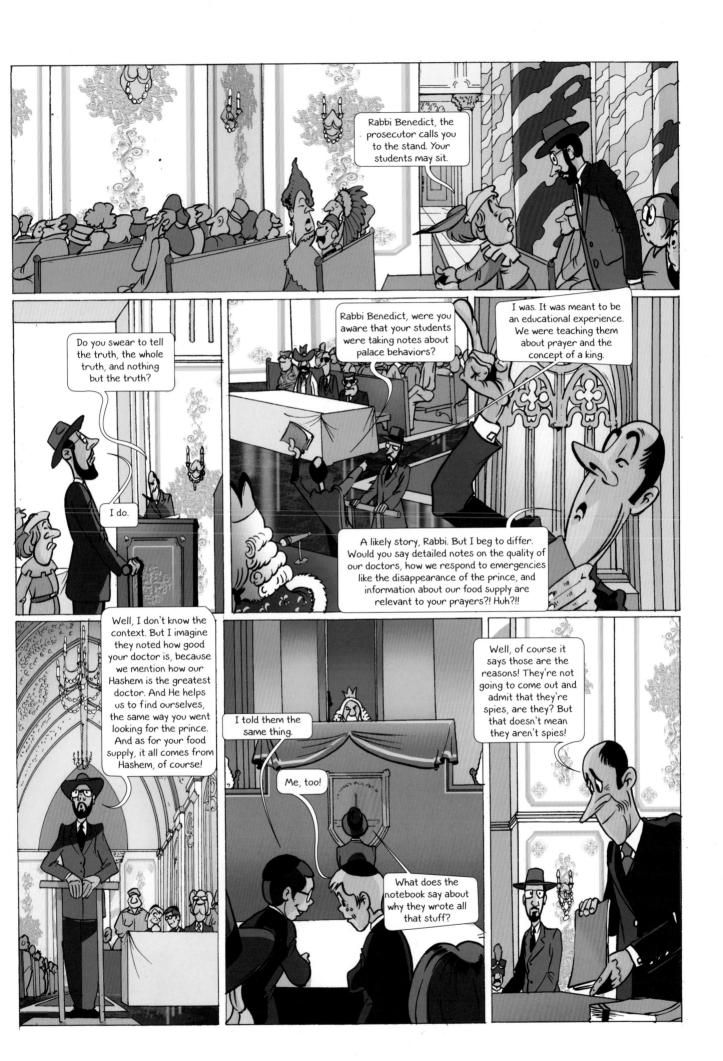

We found this piece of paper in the boys' cell yesterday.

Oh, no! It's our note!

What's he gonna do with that thing? It just tells them to be honest!

We don't know how the note was smuggled in yet, but we're working on that.

It says: "You are probably being watched. Be very careful what you say."

Does that sound like a prayer note to you, Rabbi?!

Yanky, Barotch, what do you have to say for yourselves?

Spies

Lock 'em up!

Lock up all the Jews!

IN THE KING'S PALACE   **63**

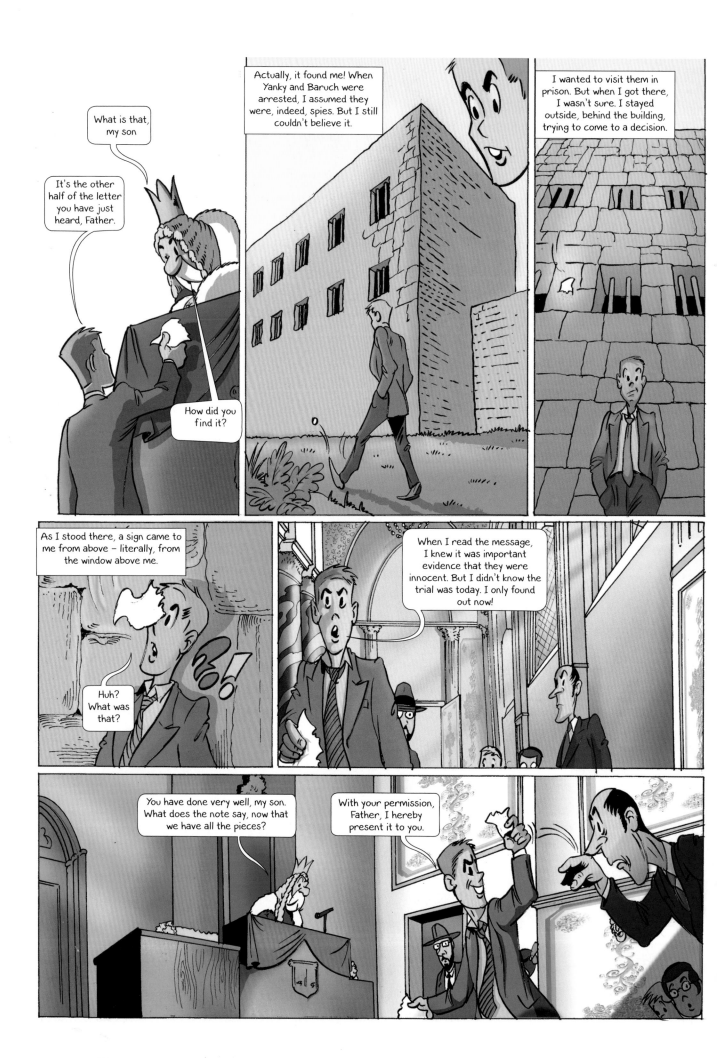

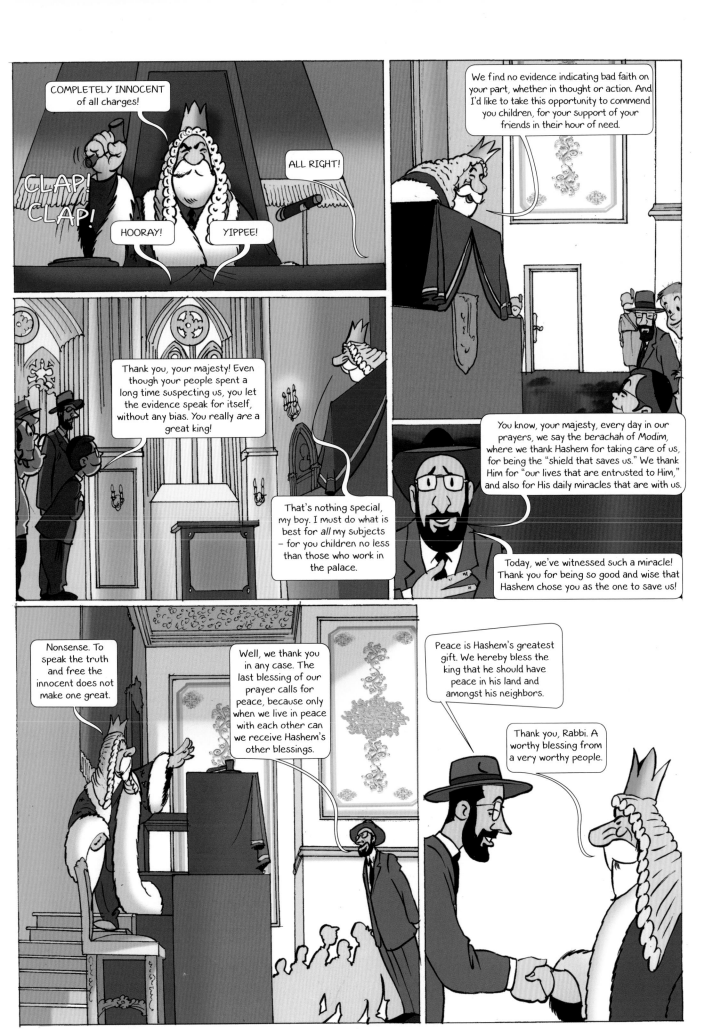

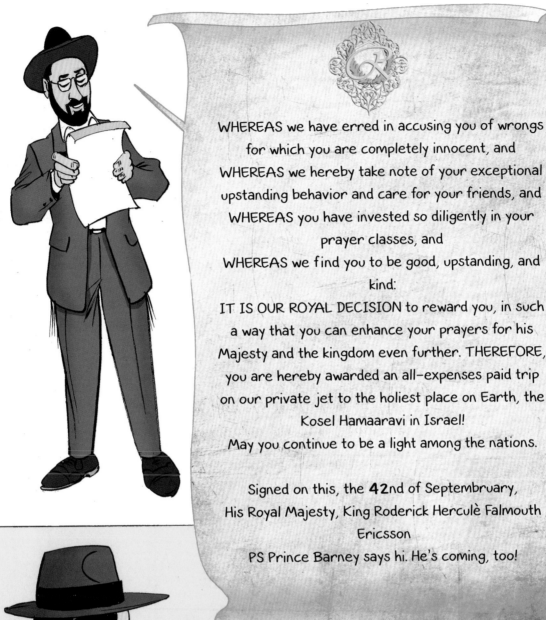

WHEREAS we have erred in accusing you of wrongs for which you are completely innocent, and
WHEREAS we hereby take note of your exceptional upstanding behavior and care for your friends, and
WHEREAS you have invested so diligently in your prayer classes, and
WHEREAS we find you to be good, upstanding, and kind:
IT IS OUR ROYAL DECISION to reward you, in such a way that you can enhance your prayers for his Majesty and the kingdom even further. THEREFORE, you are hereby awarded an all-expenses paid trip on our private jet to the holiest place on Earth, the Kosel Hamaaravi in Israel!
May you continue to be a light among the nations.

Signed on this, the **42**nd of Septembruary,
His Royal Majesty, King Roderick Herculè Falmouth Ericsson
PS Prince Barney says hi. He's coming, too!

Now turn over the page to test your knowledge in Shemoneh Esrei

See next page
for correct answer
page numbers ≫

Bracha 1 - אבות

How is mentioning the Avos in this *bracha* a praise to Hashem?

(answer on pages 13–14)

Bracha 2 - מחי׳ המתים

What does waking from a nap have to do with this *bracha*?

(answer on page 14)

Test Your Knowledge
In Shemoneh Esrei

Bracha 3 - אתה קדוש

How do we see the awesome power of Jewish children in this *bracha*?

(answer on page 16)

Bracha 4 - אתה חונן

How is this *bracha* a preparation for the next *brachos*?

(answer on page 22)

Bracha 5 - השיבנו

How is Hashem like a father that goes looking for his children?

(answer on page 28)

Bracha 6 - סלח לנו

What is special about Hashem's forgiveness?

(answer on page 31)

Bracha 7 - גואל ישראל

What do 70 hungry wolves have to do with this *bracha*?

(answer on page 33)

Bracha 8 - רפאנו

In what way is Hashem better than the best doctor?

(answer on page 34)

Bracha 9 - ברך עלינו

What is the real wonder about our food source?

(answer on pages 35 and 50)

Bracha 10 - תקע
What will happen to us when we hear Hashem blowing the great shofar?

(answer on page 39)

Bracha 11 - השיבה
What is better than having good judges?

(answer on pages 40-41)

Bracha 12 - ולמלשינים
What are two different ways Hashem will treat the goyim when Moshiach comes?

(answer on page 51)

Bracha 13 - על הצדיקים
How do we want Hashem to reward us for our trust in him?

(answer on page 53)

Bracha 14 - ולירושלים
What are three ways that Yerushalayim will be different when Moshiach comes?

(answer on pages 55-57)

Bracha 15 - את צמח
Which good idea do we get from this *bracha* about how to bring Moshiach sooner?

(answer on page 57)

Bracha 16 - שמע קולנו
We ask Hashem to "hear our voice" - does Hashem still listen to our *tefillos* even if we're too scared to *daven* with *kavana*?

(answer on page 59)

Bracha 17 - רצה
Who or what should we be excited to greet again in Yerushalayim?

(answer on page 61)

Bracha 18 - מודים
In this *bracha* what are three things we thank Hashem for?

(answer on page 71)

Bracha 19 - שים שלום
What do we need in order for all the rest of Hashem's blessings to come to us?

(answer on page 71)

Corrected Answer Pages
Bracha 1: pg 11-12	Bracha 11: pg. 38-39
Bracha 2: pg. 12	Bracha 12: pg. 49
Bracha 3: pg. 14	Bracha 13: pg. 53
Bracha 4: pg. 20	Bracha 14: pg. 54-55
Bracha 5: pg. 26	Bracha 15: pg. 55
Bracha 6: pg. 29	Bracha 16: pg. 57
Bracha 7: pg. 31	Bracha 17: pg. 59
Bracha 8: pg. 32	Bracha 18: pg. 69
Bracha 9: pg. 48	Bracha 19: pg. 69
Bracha 10: pg. 37	

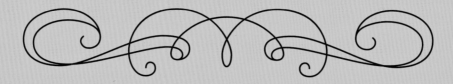

מקורות

ברכה א׳ דף 7-8 (משל לבאר השבח של הזכרת האבות) -
מאמרי בעל התניא על מאמר״זל דף תמ״ג

ברכה ב׳ דף 8 (הקשר בין ערות משינה לתחיית המתים) - מדרש איכה רבתי פ״ג

ברכה ג׳ דף 10 ("קדושים" - הם ישראל) - סדור אוצר התפלות

ברכה ד׳ דף 16 ("דעת" - להבין הי) - חידושי הרשב״א פירושי ההגדות דף נ״א

ברכה ה׳ דף 22 פשט הפשוט

ברכה ו׳ דף 25 פשט הפשוט

ברכה ז׳ דף 27 (משל מע׳ זאבים לבאר גאולתינו בכל יום) - תשובת השל״ה רנ״א א׳

ברכה ח׳ דף 28 (רפואת הנפש ורפואת הגוף) - סדור אוצר התפילות

ברכה ט׳ דף 29,44 (לזכור נפלאותיו בצמיחת הזרעים) - יסוד ושרש העבודה

ברכה י׳ דף 33 (פעולת השופר גדול) ישעי׳ כ״ז, י״ג (ופי׳ בעל התניא לקו״ת דברים דף ס׳)

ברכה י״א דף 34-35 פשט הפשוט

ברכה י״ב דף 45 (שני הנהגות עם ב׳ סוגי אומות) - סידור ר׳ יעקב מעמדין על מזמור ס״ז

ברכה י״ג דף 49 (שלא נבוש מתקותינו) - סידור אוצר התפלות (עיון תפלה)

ברכה י״ד דף 50-51 (חומת ירושלים מאש של עבודת ה׳)
- סדור אוצר התפלות (דובר שלום)

ברכה ט״ו דף 51 (כדאי שנגאל בזכות התקווה בלבד) - חיד״א, מדבר קדמות ק׳ ט״ז

ברכה ט״ז דף 53 ("שמע קולנו" - אפי׳ אם היא בלי כוונה) - סדור אוצר התפלות
(שה׳ עושה עכ״פ מדוגמת הבקשה) - של״ה הנ״ל

ברכה י״ז דף 55 פשט הפשוט

ברכה י״ח דף 65 פשט הפשוט;

ברכה י״ט דף 65 (שלום - הכלי לברכה) - עוקצין פרק ג׳ משנה י״ד

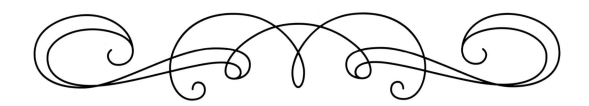

Dedicated In Loving Memory of
My Dear Parents

לזכר נשמות

יחזקאל בן אברהם אהרן

רות בת אברהם

זקלמן

עליהם השלום

By Alan & Lori Zekelman

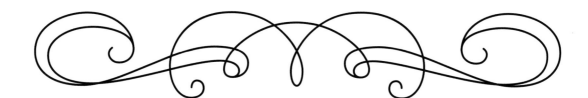

לזכר נשמת
שרה בת שמואל אייזיק

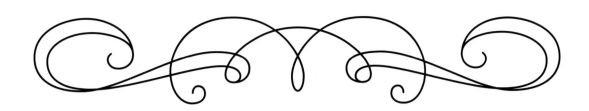

In memory of
Mrs. Chana Forta
who dedicated her life to Chinuch

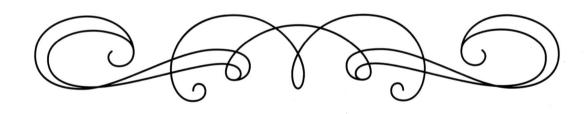

A special thank you to

יעקב יצחק נובעצקי

Dedicated by
Mendel & Shoshana Shulman

In honor of
our children &
grandchildren

May they be blessed
to be a source of
nachas to their families

In memory of
Yitschak Meir Ben Yosef Avraham

Who is certainly having so much
nachas from seeing this book
become a reality

May we merit the coming of
Moshiach Now

Yosef Chaim, Chani, Yocheved,
Chaya, Yitschak, Esther, Mendel &
Yisroel Brook

Dedicated to our
wonderful children,

**Shaina, Tuvia Dovid,
and Simcha Mendel**

Dedicated by
Ethan and Yael Gross

In memory of
Mr.& Mrs. Jack and Frieda Borsand

Dedicated by
their children
Mr.& Mrs. Gerald Borsand

לע"נ
ליבא נחמה בת יהודה ליב
ע"י אחיה ר' פייוול גדלי' קעסל

לע"נ מיכאל יעקב בן זאב וואלף ע"ה

לע"נ אסתר מלכה בת שמשון הכהן
ואליהו זלמן בן יוסף הלוי ע"ה